WILDLIFE GARDEN

Roy Vickery

THE NATURAL HISTORY MUSEUM

The germination of an idea

In the late 1980s the Natural History Museum's west garden consisted of a closely-mown lawn planted with occasional trees, mainly London plane and hawthorn. It was shielded from Cromwell Road and Queen's Gate by evergreens and towards the north by more ornamental, but rather ordinary, shrubs. It was unworthy of one of the world's greatest museums of natural history.

At about this time a number of scientists from the museum, notably botanist Clive Jermy, started to investigate the possibility of developing the garden so that it demonstrated some of the major habitats found in southern England. Five habitats were identified: a hay meadow; ponds and wetland; woodlands including coppice; hedgerow; and chalk grassland. The new Wildlife Garden would "act as an educational resource to illustrate several of the United Kingdom's principal wildlife habitats" and "provide a restful and interesting new garden as an added attraction to the museum". It would cost an estimated £60,600.

The garden takes shape; most of the basic elements - the ponds and the chalk downland are in place and await planting.

The museum's fund-raisers promoted the idea, stressing that the garden would be the museum's first living exhibition, and would provide a stimulating environment in which pupils of all abilities and their teachers could have first-hand experience of plants and animals in their natural habitats. The garden would also illustrate how habitats could be created and wildlife encouraged, on a small, inner city site. Finally, the garden could be used by museum scientists to study its colonisation, population fluctuations, the effects of air pollution, and other aspects of wildlife monitoring.

Money for the project came from a variety of sources, including 55 major sponsors, the most important being English Nature. Many other donors gave such things as trees, shrubs and wildflower seeds. In November 1994 National Tree Week was launched on the garden site, and speakers expressed their enthusiasm for the museum's initiative to "bring the countryside to central London".

Oxeye daisies, meadow buttercups and ribwort plantain thrive at the base of the chalk downland area.

Planning, planting and growing

Construction of the garden, to occupy an area of approximately one acre (or 4000 square metres), started in 1993. Many of the smaller existing trees were removed, but a number of planes, a lime and several Lombardy poplars had preservation orders on them and were retained. Because of this the new garden from the start gave an impression of maturity. However, the museum has to seek permission from the local council whenever it wants to remove, or even cut back, any of the protected trees, which can be a lengthy process. For example, when the museum wanted to remove a horse chestnut – a large, non-native tree – months of negotiation were required before it was eventually cut down. In addition to the trees, some of the shrubs beside the roads and on the north side of the garden were also preserved to help keep out traffic noise and pollution.

By July 1994 the museum's contractors had finished the landscaping of the site. In addition to the basic digging of ponds and construction of the chalk grassland mound, 29 types of rock were placed around the site. According to figures released at the time, an incredible 950 trees, 3800 shrubs and masses of

herbaceous plants were planted. The initial plantings were made during an exceptionally hot, dry spell of weather, and many people doubted if the new plants would survive.

The museum collects water from its extensive roofscape and stores it in underground tanks to be used, as far as possible, to top up the ponds. In an attempt to avoid the use of high nutrient tap water in the garden, and with the aim of reducing the museum's water bills, a 150m (490ft) deep borehole was sunk. This project was only partly successful. After analysis the water was found to be too saline for garden use, but was suitable for other needs within the museum.

Left: Young trees are planted in what will become a woodland area.

Right: The waterfall area before planting.

Above: Crab apple trees complement one of the hedgerows.

Right: The cleared area which is designated as an urban habitat and which will, hopefully, attract burrowing bees.

Far right: Bumble bees nesting in the garden November 2003. This species has been found nesting throughout the winter in southeast England.

Despite these initial problems, the plants survived, and after a year of careful nurturing the garden was ready. On 10 July, 1995, the then Secretary of State for the Environment, John Gummer, and the actress Susan Hampshire opened the garden to the public. In 1996, the Brighter Kensington and Chelsea Scheme decided that the garden should receive its Princess Alice of Athlone Environment Award and, more recently, in 2002 and 2003, the scheme has awarded the garden first prize in its wildlife garden category.

A number of meandering paths link the variety of semi-natural habitats such as can be found in southern England. Only one habitat, the acid bogland area, has been less than successful, with only bog myrtle and purple moor-grass surviving. This lack of success is almost certainly due to the area's

shady situation. A few new habitats have been introduced, including an apple orchard planted with three traditional varieties (Reverend Wilkes, Brownless Russet and Arthur Turner) and an earth bank that will provide an urban wasteland habitat for weeds (ruderals). Until recently the value of urban wasteland as a habitat for a wide range of invertebrates, including mining bees, was underrated. Growing appreciation of such sites suggested the creation of the area. Apart from the largest trees and a decreasing number of boundary shrubs (which are being removed as more appropriate native species mature), all the plants found in the garden have been introduced, or have colonised the garden since 1994.

Garden residents

Soon after planting was completed common frogs, toads and smooth newts were introduced. All three species appear to be thriving, with mature frogs and toads being spotted in damp areas or hiding under leaves and log piles, and newts being seen making their steady way through submerged water-plants throughout the summer. In order to maintain the populations of frogs, toads and newts, and to encourage a wide range of aquatic invertebrates, the museum decided not to introduce fish into the ponds.

Within two weeks of the ponds being filled they were colonised by water-fleas and many other species of microscopic aquatic animals soon followed, some introduced with water-plants, and others presumably brought in by visting

Common toads are rarely seen, but maintain a healthy population.

Ramshorn snails were abundant in the ponds during the early years, but have since become less common.

birds. Other early colonisers of the ponds included water-snails. During the garden's early years ramshorn snails were amongst the most easily observed inhabitants of the ponds; more recently their numbers have decreased and they are now rarely seen. The reasons for this rapid expansion and equally rapid decline are unknown. Pond-skaters were also seen early on and have since diminished in number. Presumably as the vegetation in the ponds has thrived and less open water is available, they have suffered as a result of the loss of preferred habitat.

Most of the animals found in the garden have found their own way in, but it was inevitable a few were inadvertently introduced with the plants. It is thought that few of these accidental introductions survive.

A popular addition to the garden in recent years has been the grey-faced Dartmoor sheep. They were brought in to graze and thus maintain the meadow and chalk grassland

Grey-faced Dartmoor sheep regularly graze and help to maintain the grassland areas.

areas. As the garden is unable to support sheep throughout the year, the sheep are shared with Freightliner's City Farm and the London Wetland Centre, which provide shelter and grazing for them when they are not in the garden.

When the sheep are absent some visitors are somewhat disappointed by the lack of mammals visible in the garden. However, such animals are rarely seen when casually visiting the country, so to put them on display, even if this was possible, would create a false impression of the English countryside.

Instead, visitors are encouraged to examine and appreciate the smaller animals and plants which account for most of Britain's wildlife, and which are often taken for granted or ignored.

Grey squirrels, native to North America, breed in the garden.

Seven species of mammal have been recorded in the garden, but they are mostly invisible when the garden is open to the public. Grey squirrels, which are native to North America rather than the British Isles, are the most frequently observed species, and in some years breed in the garden. Foxes have earths in the garden and are sometimes spotted during the day. They follow regular trails, which can be seen in the reed bed. The remaining species – the house mouse, wood mouse and two species of pipistrelle bats, the common pipistrelle and the recently distinguished soprano pipistrelle – tend to be nocturnal. Daubenton's bat is also thought to occur, but its presence needs confirmation. There are bat boxes in the garden to provide roosting places for bats. Members of the London Bat Group, who monitor the bats, say that these bat boxes are occasionally visited but are not permanently used.

The common house mouse is frequently encountered in the Museum's gardens. Wood mice have also been recorded but are rarely seen.

Maintaining a fine balance

Organic methods are used to maintain the garden, which is host to an incredibly diverse range of plants and animals bordering on Cromwell Road, one of the capital's busiest and most polluted thoroughfares. Levels of sulphur dioxide, nitrous oxide and particulates frequently exceed European Standards. Despite this, the garden provides a haven of comparative tranquility where blue tits explore the trees, damselflies appreciate the ponds and the summer scents of chalk grassland can be enjoyed. However, the garden's compact size means that everything has to be carefully

Left: The robin is one of eight species of birds known to breed in the garden.

Right: Another breeding species is the great tit.

monitored to ensure that the more vigorous species do not take over.

In order to create an impression of woodland in the shortest possible time, young trees were planted in dense stands. This has meant that each year trees that have become too big have been coppiced, pollarded or moved to different sites. Plane leaves have to be raked up, some of the more rapidly-growing water-plants need to be kept under control and alien species removed. These activities have to be carried out with great care so that the site retains its natural appearance. Few visitors realise how much skillful and ongoing manipulation is required to care for and enhance the garden's wildlife. When a visitor remarked, "This must be the most easy garden in London to maintain", she was wide of the mark, but at least she appreciated that the area did not look obviously cultivated.

*Left: Coppicing is an essential,
and popular, activity each winter.*

*Above: Volunteers use a coracle
to remove invasive vegetation
from the main pond.*

A gardener/ecologist looks after the garden with the help of a team of volunteers, including experts who help to identify the more obscure groups of animals and plants. Some of these specialists work in the museum, others come in from outside and are happy to give of their skills and expertise. Inevitably some groups of animals and plants are less well recorded than others, but there can be few other areas in the country that are so intensively monitored. Professional and amateur naturalists with expertise on the various British species are encouraged to visit the garden and record what they find. Every species recorded is entered onto a database. Thus, over the years information will accumulate and any changes in the flora and fauna of the garden can be accessed. The only comparable survey in central London is that of Buckingham Palace Garden. It is almost 40 times the area of the Natural History Museum's plot, although a great deal of it is, of course, cultivated as a standard ornamental garden that has to withstand the stress of annual garden parties and other royal events.

The plants brought into the garden were either obtained from areas under threat from development or provided by nurseries that supply plants of British origin. However, as some of the plants matured it was found that although they were the correct species, the individuals exhibited characteristics, such as peculiarly coloured flowers or aberrant habits, which suggested they had originated from places outside the British Isles. These plants have been removed and replaced by truly British forms. In recent years the gardener/ecologist has developed contacts that enable her to gather seeds with permission from sympathetic landowners, or remove plants from sites that are scheduled to be cleared for road or housing projects.

Scientists and artists use the garden for research and inspiration.

The garden through the seasons

The Wildlife Garden is an ever-changing landscape reflecting the changing seasons. The greatest activity is seen in spring and summer, and this coincides with the garden being open to the public. During the autumn and winter months the garden is much quieter, yet the seeds and fruits of various plants continue to provide food for wildlife and fallen leaves provide shelter for ground-dwelling invertebrates.

Spring

The first sign of spring in the garden is when the hazel trees extend their yellow catkins. This can be as early as January. Many plants growing on the woodland floor also flower early, before the trees come into full leaf and cast deep shade. From April onwards the woodland areas are filled with primroses, lesser celandines, daffodils, wood anemones, hawthorn, red campion and bluebells. An interesting plant that turned up in

Catkins of the goat willow emerge in spring.

2002 in the woodland area is asarabaca, an increasingly rare plant that is believed to have been an ancient introduction to the British Isles. It was recorded as being grown for medicinal use as early as 1200 (amongst other things, it was used to treat hangovers), but was not found in the wild until 1640. Other spring-flowering plants include cowslips, which thrive in the grass surrounding the largest pond.

Later in the season aquatic plants blossom, including white water-lilies and bogbean. Late spring and early summer is the time when the tadpoles of frogs and toads can easily be seen in the main pond. Newt tadpoles, which are better camouflaged and tend to stay hidden amongst the water-plants, are more difficult to spot. For a short period each year young frogs and toads can be observed as they mature from being aquatic tadpoles and emerge onto the areas surrounding the ponds. The population has grown large enough to attract the occasional passing grey heron into the garden.

Left: Smooth newts lurk in the ponds.

Top: Wood anemones form an attractive springtime carpet in the woodland area.

Middle: Bluebells and red campion make a colourful display in early summer.

Bottom: Ferns, cow parsley and garlic mustard provide patches of green and white in early summer.

Numerous microscopic animals live in the ponds. Eric Hollowday of the Quekett Microscopical Club, who regularly collects water-fleas and rotifers from the ponds, has recorded 11 species of the former and 55 species of the latter. Easier to spot in the water are the large water boatmen and back-swimmers, while damselflies and dragonflies hunt above it. Dragonflies rest with their

In summer pond-skaters are frequently seen on the surfaces of the ponds.

A harvestman rests on a nettle leaf. Not often found in central London, this is a welcome visitor.

Sawfly larvae feed on yellow iris leaves.

Azure damselflies mate on waterside vegetation.

wings outstretched, while the slower-flying damselflies rest with wings folded.

Bird activity starts early; long-tailed tits can be seen checking out suitable sites and beginning to build nests in February. Other birds seen nest-building include: greenfinches (since 2002) common blackbirds, great tits, robins, Eurasian jays, winter wrens and (since 2002) moorhens.

Summer

In summer the chalk grassland becomes bright with the yellow flowers of common toadflax and lady's bedstraw, purple thyme, shimmering quaking grass and white oxeye daisies. In the meadow purple knapweed, white yarrow and blue meadow cranesbill make a show. The bramble patch provides a home for a bramble that is widespread in southeast England, but has not yet received a scientific name.

The reed marsh, or fenland, contains a type of nettle (*Urtica dioica*) sometimes known as fen nettle, which differs from the usual stinging nettle by having greyish narrow leaves with few, if any, stinging hairs. This plant can be found in similar habitats throughout much of mainland Europe and some botanists consider it as being worthy of recognition as a separate species (*U. galeopsifolia*). However, most botanists tend to be of the opinion that since intermediates between the common nettle and the fen nettle are known, it is not appropriate to

Oxeye daisies and meadow buttercups thrive in grassland areas.

Teasels are attractive and useful as a source of food for seed-eating birds.

classify fen nettle as a separate species. Seedlings of various fruit trees, such as cherries, often turn up, presumably distributed by birds. The garden is also commonly invaded by the weedy Canadian fleabane, which has seeds adapted for wind dispersal, and the water fern which is probably carried on the feet of visiting water birds. This troublesome plant frequently needs to be removed from the ponds as it can rapidly cover large expanses of water with its tiny, water-repellant fronds.

Other noteworthy plants that tend to spring up include teasel, whose seedheads provide food for birds in autumn, herb robert, which colonises the waterfall area and the vivid blue viper's bugloss.

Throughout the summer smooth newts can usually be observed amongst submerged plants in the ponds, while dragonflies and damselflies skim over the water. Forty-four species of algae have been recorded from the main pond, but this total is lower than expected, and further monitoring will probably increase this number. Most are virtually invisible to the naked eye, but in the summer mats of filamentous algae

(*Oedogonium* sp., *Spirogyra* sp., *Mougeotia* sp.) and blanket weed disfigure the pond, and have to be removed before they threaten the survival of other water-plants. So far no solution to this problem has been found.

The chalk pond supports 38 species of algae, and the shaded upper pond has 29 species. The numbers of planktonic algae in the ponds is considered to be rather low both in terms of species and individuals. It is thought that this paucity may be due to the abundance of microscopic grazing animals, particularly water-fleas. Patches of water around the garden such as puddles also contain a rich variety of algae. In a sample collected in November 2002 the Cambridge botanists Hilary Belcher and Erica Swale identified over 60 species of algae and protozoans (microscopic single-celled organisms many of which exhibit characteristics of both animals and plants). Many of the species found colonising short-lived puddles have not yet been recorded in the ponds,

Some summers the main pond becomes covered with an algal mat which needs to be removed.

and amongst them Dr Belcher and Dr Swale found the colourless flagellate *Gyromitus disomatus*, which is extremely rare. Preliminary results of a survey of below-ground soil algae suggest that the lowland heath area is dominated by a variety of green algae, while blue-green algae dominate the chalk downland.

Lichens are also found in the garden. These are complex organisms that consist of a fungus living in intimate association with an alga. As they are extremely sensitive to air pollution, it is inevitable that the majority of the 28 lichen species that have so far been recorded are those which are characteristic of polluted areas. A small number of lichen species were brought into the garden on the bark of introduced trees, but these failed to survive.

Dense duckweed shades out other vegetation thus upsetting the ecology of the main pond.

Others are restricted to the garden's boundary walls. Most of these pollution-tolerant species are small and are noticed only by people with a specialist interest. However, air pollution in London is changing and the amount of sulphur dioxide – the pollutant most harmful to lichens – is decreasing as a result of the reduction of industry and coal-burning domestic fires. Consequently, the lichen flora of the garden is gradually increasing. Ironically, the pollution-tolerant lichen, *Lecanora conizaeoides* has declined to the extent that it has almost vanished from the garden. The main pollutants believed to inhibit future lichen colonisation and growth are particulates and oxides of nitrogen, which are produced by road traffic. Since the central London congestion charge was introduced in February 2003 the number of vehicles using the roads around the museum has significantly decreased.

So far it is too early to know what effect this will have on lichens and other pollution-sensitive organisms in the garden.

The great hairy willowherb thrives in damp areas of the garden.

Top left: Ramsons, also known as wild garlic, is an attractive flower in the woodland areas.

Top: Bladder campion pops up beside paths.

Left: Scabious grows on the chalk downland.

Ten permanent 10 x 15 cm (4 x 6 in) quadrats have been established on rock and brick substrate, and they will be regularly photographed, so that changes in their lichen communities can be assessed. Another project has involved bringing in lichen-covered branches from comparatively unpolluted areas and noting how the species on these branches react to London's pollution. As might be expected most of them rapidly sicken and die. It appears that the rapid demise of these lichens was also brought about by tits and other birds which appreciate them as a source of nesting material.

Common spotted orchid on chalk mound; a project to establish orchids in the garden was started in spring 2003.

Over 350 species of beetle, including the predatory devil's coach-horse have been recorded in the garden. Martin Honey of the museum's entomology department has enthusiastically monitored the garden's butterflies and moths, recording a total of 462 species. These include two that are new to the British Isles: *Ectoedemia heringella*, a minute leaf-miner on holm oak, and *Prays citri*, which is a pest of citrus crops in the Mediterranean region and is considered to be an accidental, non-breeding introduction.

Most of the garden's moths are small, night-flying species, but more conspicuous and day-flying species include the six-spot burnet moth, which breeds in the chalk grassland. Spectacular night-fliers include the elephant hawkmoth and poplar hawkmoth. In 2003 a caterpillar of the humming-bird hawkmoth was found – a welcome addition to the moths that breed in the garden.

Left: Marsh marigolds and ragged robins thrive in damp patches.

Right: A male common blue searches a bird's-foot trefoil flower for nectar.

Left: This species of hoverfly is often seen feeding on nectar and its larvae feed on aphids, making it beneficial as both a pollinator and pest controller.

Right: Brambles provide cover and food for birds.

So far 19 species of butterflies have been recorded. These include the holly blue, which is the only butterfly known to breed in the garden, and such showy and well-known species as red admiral, peacock, common blue and orange tip. Buddleias (also known as butterfly bushes) have colonised the east boundary of the garden and although these are native to China rather than the British Isles some have been allowed to remain so that their flowers can provide food for butterflies and moths. Presumably some of these moths and butterflies provide food for the garden's 17 recorded species of spiders. Although none of the spiders is considered to be particularly rare, the number of species exceeds that which would be expected in central London.

All five of southern England's most common woodlice thrive in the garden, and the land hopper was first recorded in 1999. This species is native to Australia, but since the early 1980s has been turning up in leaf litter in the south of England. There appear to be few species of tardigrades, or 'water bears', which are microscopic invertebrates. So far these have been under-recorded in the garden, and, indeed throughout London as a whole. There are about 90-100 species in the British Isles of which only three have been confidently identified in the garden. This compares with the 11 species collected on a single visit in May 1996 to the more mature and more extensive gardens of Buckingham Palace.

Far left: Moorhens breed in the main pond.

Left: An island with a waterfowl nesting box placed in the main pond to encourage birds to nest away from predatory foxes.

Damp summer evenings entice the garden's resident slugs and snails into the open. A total of 27 species have been found in the garden. Some of these, which were unintentionally introduced with plants, have become extinct and the slugs and snails currently found form a similar population to that found in most city gardens.

In summer thick foliage makes it difficult to observe birds, but they can be heard in the trees. Early in the day, or during quiet periods, they may be seen searching for insects. Fifty-six birds have been observed in, or flying over, the garden. However, the most conspicuous of the birds that breed in the garden are the common moorhens which raised two broods in

2003. Ground-nesting birds are liable to fox depredation, but the moorhens have had their chances of survival increased by the provision of a nesting box on a small island in the main pond, constructed by volunteers. These plucky little birds provide an attraction to visitors. Mallards have also successfully raised broods in the main pond.

In July 2002 winter wrens built a nest in the eaves of the gardener's hut; by August the chicks had fledged. Other breeding birds include wood pigeon, European robin, common blackbird (which nests in the hedge beside the lane), blue tit and great tit (both of which use nest-boxes), Eurasian jay, and starling. Song thrushes nested in the garden during the first few years but sadly this nationally declining species has not bred in the garden since 1999. In addition to the provision of nest-boxes, there is also a bird-feeding station. All of the species that breed in the garden commonly breed elsewhere in the London area.

Left: Nesting boxes are attached to the garden's mature trees

Above: A wren makes its nest in the eaves of the gardener's hut.

Autumn

Piles of decaying logs placed in the woodland areas encourage the growth of toadstools and provide food for wood-boring insects. Autumn is the best time to observe and identify the garden's population of fungi, as this is when many of them bear their fruiting bodies ('toadstools'). Often the fruiting bodies are present for very short periods and consequently they have been under-recorded. Over 150 species of toadstools and similar fungi have been recorded and 97 species of smaller fungi, such as powdery mildews and rusts have been found growing on herbaceous plants, shrubs and trees. Taking into account its rich diversity, mycologists at the Royal Botanic Gardens, Kew estimate that the number of fungi to be found in the garden should exceed 2000 species.

Orange and pink spindle fruits
provide colour in autumn when
most flowers are fading.

As autumn proceeds the trees begin to lose their leaves and the ground level vegetation dies back. Few plants are in flower at this time but some have equally colourful and conspicuous fruits. Particularly attractive are the pink and orange fruits of the spindle bushes. The hedge is also a rich habitat at this time of year, with the bright red hips of dog rose and the poisonous red berries of honeysuckle. The long, plume-like styles of old man's beard give the seed heads the hoary, grey appearance indicated by the name.

The seeds and berries attract foraging birds into the garden. A grey wagtail has become a regular autumn visitor (from late September to January) and in 2001 it was heard and occasionally seen during the summer. In September 2002 a reed warbler was spotted around the pond and in 2003 a willow warber was seen. Flocks of long-tailed tits are frequently seen in early autumn right through the winter, until January/February when they pair off to breed.

Rotting logs provide a habitat for a variety of fungi, including common bonnet and cloud mushrooms.

Winter

Bryophytes – mosses and liverworts – are attractive and ecologically important but tend to be overlooked by casual visitors, especially as they are most easily seen during the winter months when the garden is not regularly open to the public. However, a total of 49 moss and seven liverwort species have been recorded, not all of them being present every year. A few mosses, such as sphagnum, were deliberately introduced in what was considered to be appropriate habitats, but have failed to survive. Other mosses that are early colonisers of bare ground have also come and gone as more vigorous plants have taken over their habitats as part of the natural cycle of vegetation development.

The garden has a number of mature holly trees that produce quantities of berries each year, providing several bird species with a source of winter food. In November 2002, redwing were twice spotted feeding off the holly berries.

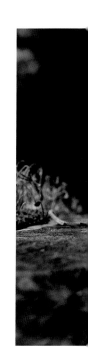

When more vigorous plants have died back, the subtle attractions of bryum mosses can be enjoyed.

54

On rare occasions snow covers the garden; all looks still, but life continues under the temporary white blanket.

Enjoying the garden

The garden is open to the public throughout the summer months, and guides are available to explain the various habitats. New uses for the garden are continually being explored. Regular activities for school groups include mini-beast safaris that help children to become familiar with a range of invertebrates using simple keys to identify them, a workshop exploring the diversity of leaf-shapes, and the ever popular pond-dipping. In a year, approximately 700 children from 15 schools have participated in such activities; similarly, 40 workshops for schools and an additional 54 workshops for families with primary school-aged children were arranged.

During the summer, tours of the garden are led by trained guides who discuss themes such as British habitats and their flora and fauna, scientists' experiments, colonisation, and pollution. Pre-booked tours are more popular, but are usually limited to 15 participants. The small number of people taking part in tours encourages interaction between the guides and their audiences, leading to shared experiences and the exchange of information. Occasionally museum scientists lead tours relating to their research interests. Here again contributions from the public are encouraged and can provide valuable leads. This is particularly worthwhile when topics like the use of wild plants in medicine are being discussed. Often the scientist receives almost as much information as he or she gives out.

Other events for adults include coppicing and hedge-laying days, opportunities to spin and dye wool from the museum's sheep, and an introduction to the identification of wildflowers. Less formal activities for adults include the work undertaken by a wide range of volunteers who enjoy central London's fragment of countryside. Volunteers regularly help with monitoring plants and animals, weeding and composting, building fences, caring for sheep, clearing ponds of

Numerous school parties visit to enjoy pond-dipping and similar activities.

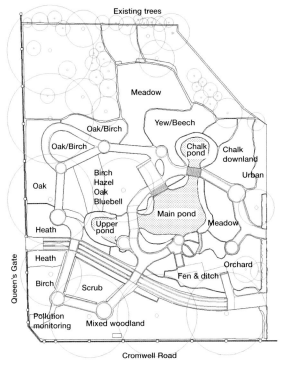

Existing trees

Meadow

Oak/Birch

Yew/Beech

Oak/Birch

Chalk pond

Chalk downland

Oak

Birch
Hazel
Oak
Bluebell

Urban

Main pond

Meadow

Heath

Upper pond

Orchard

Heath

Fen & ditch

Queen's Gate

Birch

Scrub

Pollution monitoring

Mixed woodland

Cromwell Road

Plan of the garden showing the layout of its habitats.

aggressive plants, raking fallen leaves, and being on hand during the garden's special open days.

Each year the garden is open on two Sundays in aid of the National Gardens Scheme, which raises money for a variety of charities. The first of these open afternoons takes place in April, when visitors have the opportunity to enjoy spring flowers before the garden is regularly open to the public. The second afternoon is held early in July. On both afternoons plants, books and teas are on sale, and a number of museum scientists give talks about their specialist interests. These include London's changing flora, moths in the garden, and the uses of wild plants.

In 2003 the garden also held a special open afternoon as part of the Henry Doubleday Research Association's open organic gardens programme. Also in 2003, on 28 June, the garden hosted Londoners' first Wildlife Gardening Day. Botanist David Bellamy supported the day, and a number of experts were on hand running workshops, which included the sustainable management of slugs and snails and how to develop a bat-friendly garden. The event overflowed from the garden on to the adjacent lawn, where a wildlife-garden fair was held with various conservation groups setting up stalls. The day was fully booked and provided food for thought and inspiration to all those who attended.

Smaller, semi-public, events include visits from local natural history societies at which participants are encouraged to record any unusual species that they observe. Even in an area that is well recorded, a fresh pairs of eyes, ears or nostrils can notice species that more regular recorders have overlooked. Bearing this in mind, a series of half-day recording workshops were started. These are intended to bring together museum scientists and external experts to examine the garden and study under-recorded groups. For example, the number of plant galls recorded in the garden more than doubled after such a workshop in September 2003. Of particular interest was the ram's-horn gall, which occurs on oak trees and is caused by the gall wasp. This was first recorded in the British Isles in Berkshire in 1997 and has rapidly become widespread in and around London.

Led by the wildlife gardener/ecologist, and supported by a scientific advisory group, the museum seeks to make its garden more accessible and enjoyable to an ever-widening public in the hope that they will increase their appreciation of native plants and animals. The garden inspires and challenges visiting garden-owners to explore ways in which they can make their own gardens more attractive to a greater variety of wild species. A high proportion of London's 'green lungs' consists of private gardens; the Natural History Museum's Wildlife Garden demonstrates what can be achieved in a small space with busy roads forming two of its boundaries.

APPENDIX

(The following list gives the scientific names for species recorded in this book.)

Asarabaca, *Asarum europaeum*

Azure damselfly,
  Coenagrion puella

Back-swimmer, *Notonecta* sp.

Bird's-foot trefoil,
  Lotus corniculatus

Bladder campion, *Silene vulgaris*

Blanket weed,
  Cladophora glomerata

Blue tit, *Parus caeruleus*

Bluebell,
  Hyacinthoides nonscripta

Bog myrtle, *Myrica gale*

Bogbean, *Menyanthes trifoliata*

Bramble, *Rubus* spp.

Bryum moss, *Bryum capillare*

Bumble bee, *Bombus lucorum;*
  Bombus terrestris

Butterfly bush, *Buddleja davidii*

Canadian fleabane,
  Conyza canadensis

Cherry, *Prunus* cvs.

Cloud mushroom,
  Trametes versicolor

Common blackbird,
  Turdus merula

Common blue butterfly,
  Polyommatus icarus

Common bonnet fungus,
  Mycena galericulata

Common frog, *Rana temporaria*

Common house mouse,
  Mus domesticus

Common moorhen,

Gallinula chloropus

Common pipistrelle,
  Pipistrellus pipistrellus

Common spotted orchid,
  Dactylorhiza fuchsii

Common toad, *Bufo bufo*

Common toadflax,
  Linaria vulgaris

Cow parsley,
  Anthiscus sylvestris

Cowslip, *Primula veris*

Crab apple,
  Malus sylvestris

Daffodil, *Narcissus*
  pseudonarcissus

Daubenton's bat,
  Myotis daubentonii

Devil's coach-horse,
  Staphylinus olens

Dog rose, *Rosa canina*

Elephant hawkmoth,
  Deilephila elpenor

Eurasian jay,
  Garrulus glandarius

European robin,
  Erithacus rubecula

Fen nettle, *Urtica galeopsifolia*

Filamentous algae,
  Oedogonium spp., *Spirogyra*
  spp., *Mougeotia* spp.

Fox, *Vulpes vulpes*

Gall wasp, *Andricus aries*

Garlic mustard, *Alliaria petiolata*

Goat willow, *Salix caprea*

Great hairy willowherb,
  Epilobium hirsutum

Great tit, *Parus major*

Greenfinch, *Carduelis chloris*

Grey heron, *Ardea cinerea*

Grey squirrel,
  Sciurus carolinensis

Grey wagtail, *Motacilla cinerea*

Harvestman,
  Leiobunum rotundum

Hawthorn,
  Crataegus monogyna

Hazel, *Corylus avellana*

Herb robert,
  Geranium robertianum

Holly blue butterfly, *Celastrina*
  argiolus

Holm oak, *Quercus ilex*

Honeysuckle,
  Lonicera periclymenum

Horse chestnut,
  Aesculus hippocastanum

Hoverfly, *Syrphus ribesii*

Humming-bird hawkmoth,
  Macroglossum stellatarum

Knapweed, *Centaurea nigra*

Lady's bedstraw, *Galium verum*

Land hopper,
  Arcitalitrus dorrieni

Lesser celandine,
  Ranunculus ficaria

Lime, *Tilia* sp.

Lombardy poplar, *Populus nigra cv.*

London plane,

Platanus x hispanica

Long-tailed tit,
Aegithalos caudatus

Mallard, *Anas platyrhynchos*

Marsh marigold,
Caltha palustris

Meadow buttercup,
Ranunculus acris

Meadow cranesbill,
Geranium pratense

Navelwort, *Umbilicus rupestris*

Old man's beard,
Clematis vitalba

Orange tip butterfly,
Anthocharis cardamines

Oxeye daisy,
Leucanthemum vulgare

Peacock butterfly, *Inachis io*

Pond-skater, *Gerris* sp.

Poplar hawkmoth,
Laothoe populi

Primrose, *Primula vulgaris*

Purple moor-grass,

Molinia caerulea

Quaking grass, *Briza media*

Ramshorn snail, *Anisus vortex*

Ramsons (wild garlic),
Allium ursinum

Red admiral, *Vanessa atalanta*

Red campion, *Silene dioica*

Redwing, *Turdus iliacus*

Reed warbler, *Acrocephalus scirpaceus*.

Ribwort plantain,
Plantago lanceolata

Scabious, *Scabiosa columbaria*

Six-spot burnet moth,
Zygaena filipendulae

Smooth newt, *Triturus vulgaris*

Song thrush, *Turdus philomelos*

Soprano pipistrelle,
Pipistrellus pygmus

Spindle, *Euonymus europaeus*

Starling, *Sturnus vulgaris*

Stinging nettle, *Urtica dioica*

Teasel, *Dipsacus fullonum*

Thyme, *Thymus vulgaris*

Viper's bugloss, *Echium vulgare*

Water boatman, *Hesperocorixa* sp.

Water fern, *Azolla filiculoides*

Water-flea, *Daphnia* sp.

White water-lily, *Nymphaea alba*

Willow warbler,
Phylloscopus trochilus

Winter wren,
Troglodytes troglodytes

Wood anemone,
Anemone nemorosa

Wood mouse,
Apodemus sylvaticus

Wood pigeon,
Columba palumbus

Yarrow,
Achillea millefolium

Yellow iris,
Iris pseudacorus

Author's acknowledgements

We thank numerous museum scientists, archivists, photographers, non-museum specialists and reviewers for their assistance, and in particular thank the gardener/ecologist Caroline Ware.

First published by the Natural History, Museum, Cromwell Road, London SW7 5BD
© 2004, The Natural History Museum, London
ISBN 0-565-09185-9

Edited by: Celia Coyne
Designed by: NHM Design Studio
Reproduction and printing by: Craft Print, Singapore